Jennelle St. Marie M.A.
Illustrations John Gamades

OSM, Inc.
9050 Parley Lake Road
Waconia, MN 55387
(952)442-7052

Not long ago in a very cold place,

lived a clever, small boy
and his magical mates.

and 3 ferrets who
loved to snuggle in his lap.

His mates were not magical
because of special powers they had.

They simply listened to
both their hearts and their heads.

Many might argue that
his mates were not smart

but the boy knew it only looked that way to those missing their hearts.

Their hearts were not lost forever,

just misplaced for a while,

giving their heads time to rummage through this and that pile.

So his mates gently whispered,

They will find their misplaced hearts once they slow down their hurry.

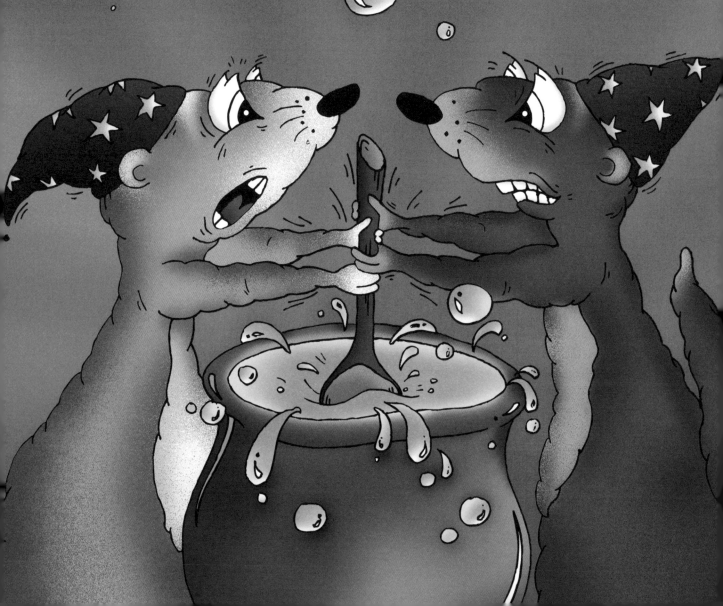

and some will pop up
quite strange and brand new.

Others will feel so wonderful you'll want to grab on and hold tight

but they will slip from your grasp like dreams in the night.

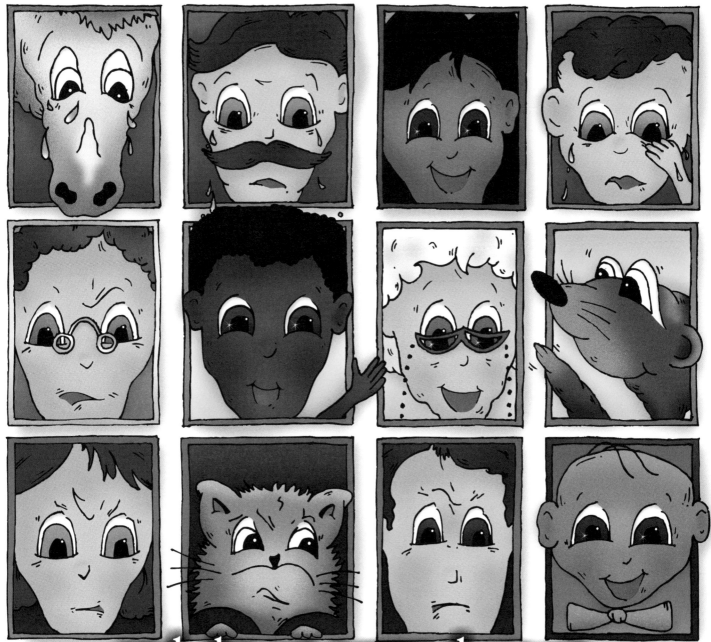

and almost never show up
neatly arranged in rows.

They are simply experiences
only you have had.

Feelings are grand
because they give big clues

most importantly about what
is happening inside of you.

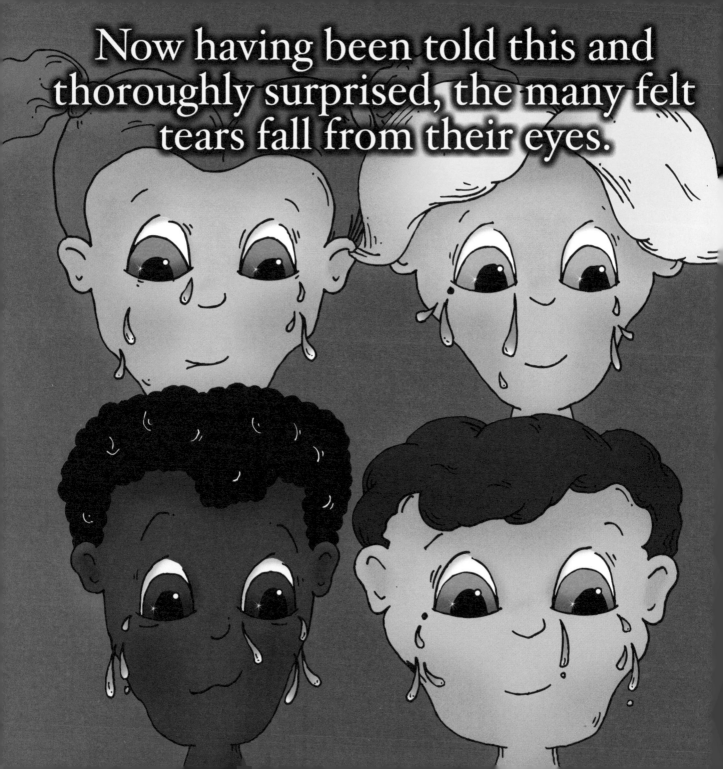

in fact the opposite, it was the most wonderful news the many ever had.

For then they all knew,
as the boy and his mates

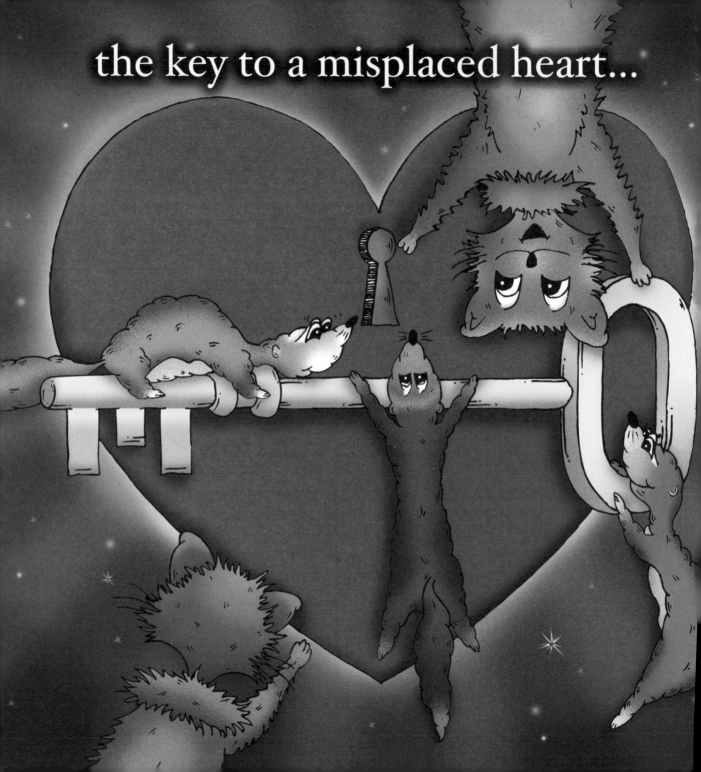